CANADIAN CURRICULUM PRESS
Forward Learning

Math

W9-CAX-887

Grade 3

Table of Contents

$423 - 139 = 284$

$28 \div 4 = 7$

$765 + 476 = 1241$

$5 \times 7 = 35$

- Addition, subtraction, multiplication, division
- Fractions
- Canadian money and time
- Geometry, graphs and probability
- And much more!

Elaine J. Kenny, B.Ed.

Number Order

Print the numbers in order from least to greatest.

426, 725, 619, 443   426, 443, 619, 725

673, 947, 813, 999   673, 813, 947, 999

311, 342, 421, 299   299, 311, 342, 421

703, 698, 896, 799   698, 703, 799, 896

812, 99, 999, 499   99, 499, 812, 999

Print the missing numbers. Watch for skip counting!

114 115 116 117 118 119 120 121 122 123

402 403 404 405 406 407 408 409 410 411

667 668 669 670 671 672 673 674 675

310 320 330 340 350 360 370 380 390 400

940 942 944 946 948 950 952 954 956 958

Thousands, Hundreds, Tens, and Ones

Example:

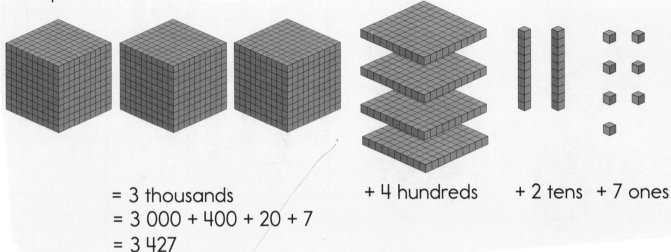

= 3 thousands
= 3 000 + 400 + 20 + 7
= 3 427

+ 4 hundreds   + 2 tens   + 7 ones

Count and print the number of thousands, hundreds, tens, and ones on the lines below.

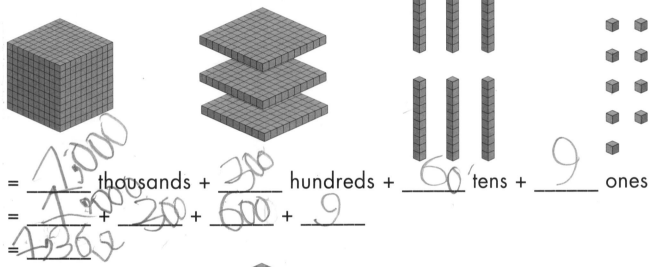

= __1,000__ thousands + __300__ hundreds + __60__ tens + __9__ ones

= __1,000__ + __300__ + __600__ + __9__

= __1,360__

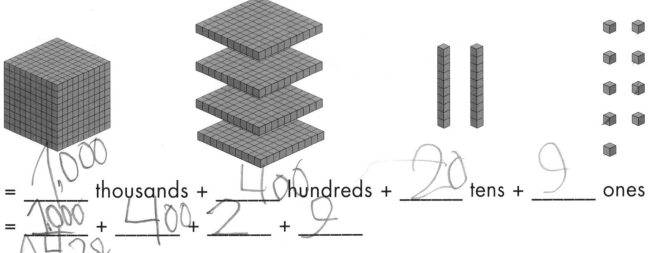

= __1,000__ thousands + __400__ hundreds + __20__ tens + __9__ ones

= __1000__ + __400__ + __2__ + __9__

= __1429__

3

Thousands, Hundreds, Tens, and Ones

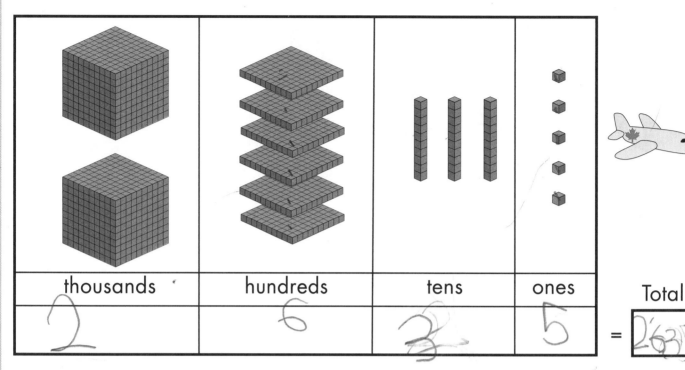

thousands	hundreds	tens	ones	Total
2	6	3	5	= 2635

Follow the instructions for each number.

6 23① Circle the ones.

4 1⑤6 Circle the tens.

3 ⑨15 Circle the hundreds.

⑧121 Circle the thousands.

1 ⑤46 Circle the hundreds.

⑤767 Circle the thousands.

9 0⓪0 Circle the tens.

1 ①11 Circle the hundreds.

What is the place value of the **green** digit? Circle the answer.

1 69**3**	thousands	hundreds	tens	(ones)
4 7**9**4	thousands	hundreds	(tens)	ones
6 **1**11	thousands	(hundreds)	tens	ones
9 42**3**	thousands	hundreds	tens	(ones)
4 199	(thousands)	hundreds	tens	ones
3 6**6**0	thousands	hundreds	(tens)	ones

Expanded Notation

Example:
Expanded notation using **words**.
4 872 = 4 thousands + 8 hundreds + 7 tens + 2 ones

Example:
Expanded notation using **digits**.
4 872 = 4000 + 800 + 70 + 2

Use **words** to show the numbers in expanded notation.

693 = _____ 6 hundreds _____ + _9 tens_ + _3 ones_

1 314 = _7 thousands_ + _3 hundred_ _7 tens_ + _4 ones_

4 643 = _4 thousands_ + _6 hundreds_ + _4 tens_ + _3 ones_

798 = _7 hundreds_ + _9 tens_ + _8 ones_

Use **digits** to show the numbers in expanded notation.

451 = _____ 400 _____ + _50_ + _1_

1 846 = _1000_ + _800_ + _40_ + _6_

4 970 = _4000_ + _900_ + _70_ + _0_

323 = _300_ + _20_ + _3_

5

Addition Without Regrouping

When we add, we find the sum. First we add the ones, then the tens, and then the hundreds.

Add the ones:

```
  32 5
+ 26 1
─────────
     6
```

Next add the tens:

```
  3 2 5
+ 2 6 1
─────────
   8 6
```

Next add the hundreds:

```
  3 2 5
+ 2 6 1
─────────
  5 8 6
```

Try these.

```
  1 2 6          4 6          6 8
+ 3 5 2        + 3 3        + 2 1
```

```
  3 1 1        1 3 2          6 3 1
+ 4 6 7      + 2 2 5        + 3 2 4
```

Addition With Regrouping

When the sum in any column is greater than 9, we need to regroup that number. See how this works in this example:

```
  1
  7 8
+ 5 6
───────
    4
```

We add the ones column, 8+6=14. Since 14 is greater than 9, we have to regroup it into 1 ten and 4 ones. We put the 4 ones into the ones place and the 1 ten into the tens place.

```
1 1
  7 8
+ 5 6
───────
  3 4
```

Now we add the tens, 1+7+5=13. We have to regroup the 13 tens into 1 hundred and 3 tens. We put the 3 tens into the tens place and the 1 hundred into the hundreds place.

```
1 1
  7 8
+ 5 6
───────
1 3 4
```

Finally we add the hundreds. 1+0=1. We have found the sum, 134.

Hint: Be sure to keep the numbers lined up in the right place value column.

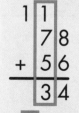

Add:

25 +36	26 +48	156 +27	816 +159
78 +15	71 +19	321 +88	267 +247
43 +48	84 +17	477 +183	699 +128
75 +25	37 +57	765 +476	575 +426

32 +88	31 +79	15 +98	33 +97	85 +69
39 +84	89 +58	24 +96	85 +97	82 +48
43 +67	49 +94	51 +69	95 +99	91 +87

Subtraction Without Regrouping

When we subtract, we find the difference. First we subtract the ones, then the tens, and then the hundreds.

```
  7 5 9        7 5 9        7 5 9
 -2 4 3       -2 4 3       -2 4 3
      6         1 6        5 1 6
```

Try these.

```
   1 9          5 6          3 3
  -1 7         -2 1         -1 2
```

```
   9 8          8 6          4 6
  -7 4         -5 5         -1 4
```

Subtraction With Regrouping

When we subtract, sometimes we have to regroup. See how this works in this example.

```
   4 5
 -  2 7
 ─────
```
We start with the ones. Since we can't subtract 7 from 5, we need to regroup. We take 1 ten from the tens place and add it to the 5 ones so that we now have 15 ones and 3 tens.

Now we can subtract the ones column, 15-7=8.

Next, we subtract the tens column.

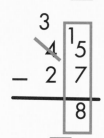

Since we regrouped 1 ten away from the 4 tens, there are 3 tens left. We subtract 3-2=1. Now we have found the difference, 18.

Subtract:

1. 355
    −143

4. 186
    −169

7. 618
    −332

10. 378
    −298

2. 725
    −412

5. 890
    −271

8. 644
    −427

11. 467
    −121

3. 967
    −132

6. 579
    −176

9. 399
    −386

12. 471
    −330

Subtraction

Add and subtract to solve the word problems.

Jeff has 363 hockey cards and Jake has 193 hockey cards.

a. How many hockey cards
   do the boys have in all?

b. How many more hockey cards
   does Jeff have than Jake?

_____ hockey cards

_____ more

Rohan has 423 buttons. Jamari has 96 fewer buttons than Rohan.

a. How many buttons
   does Jamari have?

b. How many buttons do
   the boys have in all?

_____ buttons

_____ buttons

Look at the cost of skates.

a. What is the price difference between the skates? $ _____

b. What is the total cost of both pairs of skates? $ _____

Multiplication

Multiplication is a way to add numbers faster. Multiplication is adding the same number together multiple times. When numbers are multiplied, the answer is called the **product**.

Example:

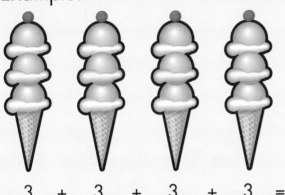

How many scoops of ice cream are there?

$$3 + 3 + 3 + 3 = 12$$
$$4 \text{ groups of } 3 \text{ scoops} = 12$$
$$4 \times 3 = 12$$

$\underline{3}$ + $\underline{3}$ + $\underline{3}$ + $\underline{3}$ = $\underline{12}$

Complete the addition and multiplication sentences.

How many petals?

__ + __ + __ = ____
__ groups of 5 petals = ____
__ × __ = ____
There are ___ petals.

How many bees?

__ + __ + __ + __ + __ + __ = ____
___ groups of 2 bees = ____
__ × __ = ____
There are ___ bees.

How many ladybugs?

__ + __ + __ + __ + __ = ____
___ groups of 4 ladybugs = ____
__ × __ = ____
There are ___ ladybugs.

How many butterflies?

__ + __ + __ + __ + __ + __ = ____
___ groups of 3 butterflies = ____
__ × __ = ____
There are ___ butterflies.

Multiplication

Look at the pictures. Fill in the blanks.

_4_ groups of _8_ crayons

= _4_ x _8_

= _32_

___ groups of ___ pennies

= ___ x ___

= ___

___ groups of ___ peas in pod

= ___ x ___

= ___

___ groups of ___ beans

= ___ x ___

= ___

Write a multiplication sentence to match each group of beads.

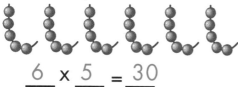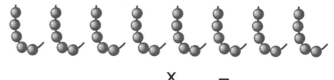

_6_ x _5_ = _30_

___ x ___ = ___

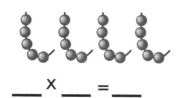

___ x ___ = ___

___ x ___ = ___

Practice multiplication tables.

1 x 2 = ___	1 x 5 = ___	1 x 3 = ___	1 x 7 = ___
2 x 2 = ___	2 x 5 = ___	2 x 3 = ___	2 x 7 = ___
3 x 2 = ___	3 x 5 = ___	3 x 3 = ___	3 x 7 = ___
4 x 2 = ___	4 x 5 = ___	4 x 3 = ___	4 x 7 = ___
5 x 2 = ___	5 x 5 = ___	5 x 3 = ___	5 x 7 = ___
6 x 2 = ___	6 x 5 = ___	6 x 3 = ___	6 x 7 = ___
7 x 2 = ___	7 x 5 = ___	7 x 3 = ___	7 x 7 = ___

Division

Division is equal sharing or grouping. The answer to the question is called a **quotient**.

Example:
How many baseballs in all? _20_
How many groups are there? _4_
This shows 20 ÷ 4 = 5

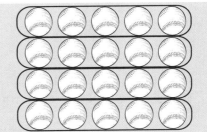

How many are there in total? _____
You can eat 3 apples a day.
Circle groups of 3.
How many groups are there? _____
How many days will it take you
to eat all the apples? _____
Write a division sentence.

_____

How many are there in total?_____
You can put 4 balls in each bin.
Circle groups of 4.
How many groups are there? _____
How many bins do you need? _____
Write a division sentence.

_____

How many are there in total? _____
You want to give 2 each to some friends.
Circle in groups of 2.
How many groups of 2? _____
How many friends can you give
2 marbles to? Write a division sentence.

_____

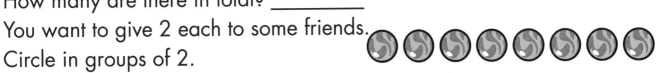

Division

Draw the equal groupings. Fill in the blanks. The first one is done.

Divide 20 pencils equally among 4 backpacks.

There are ___5___ pencils in each backpack.

$20 \div 4 = $ ___5___

Hint: Draw one pencil at a time in each backpack. Count as you go until you have drawn 20 pencils.

Divide 15 frogs equally onto 5 lilypads.

There are _____ frogs on each lilypad.

$15 \div 5 = $ _____

Divide 12 oranges equally into 4 bowls.

There are _____ oranges in each bowl.

$12 \div 4 = $ _____

Divide 12 balloons equally to 3 children.

Each child has _____ balloons.

$12 \div 3 = $ _____

Fractions

Fractions tell about equal parts of a whole or set.

$\dfrac{2}{5}$ **Numerator** **Denominator**

There are 5 parts to this whole. 2 parts are shaded.

The **denominator** is the bottom number in a fraction. It tells how many parts there are in total in the whole or set. In this case the denominator is 5. The **numerator** is the top number in a fraction. It is the number of equal parts being identified. In this case the numerator is 2.

The line separating the numerator and denominator means 'out of'. This fraction is $\frac{2}{5}$. It means 2 equal parts 'out of' 5 total parts.

Pizza Parts

Look at the pizza.
Some slices have pepperoni,
some have mushrooms,
some have olives,
and some are plain.

Answer the questions
about the parts of the pizza.

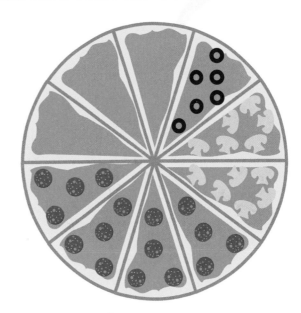

1. How many slices of pizza are there in total? _____

2. What fraction of the pizza is plain? _____

3. What fraction has pepperoni? _____

4. What fraction has olives? _____

5. What fraction has mushrooms? _____

Fractions

Write a fraction that identifies the coloured part of each shape.

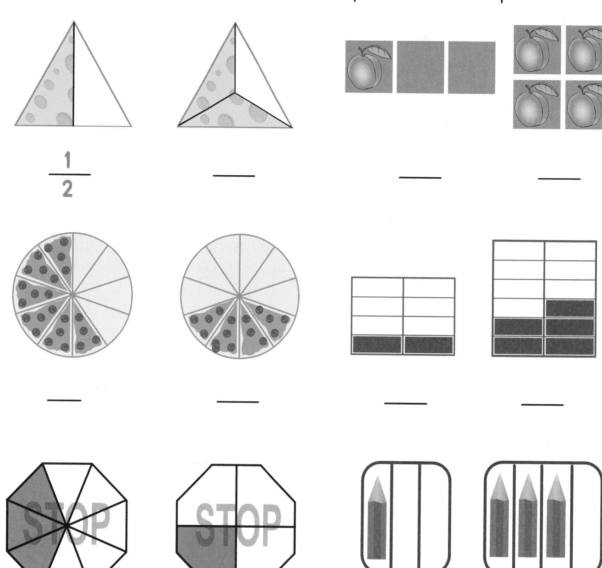

$\dfrac{1}{2}$ ___   ___   ___

___   ___   ___   ___

___   ___   ___   ___

___   ___   ___   ___

Number Sense and Numeration

Canadian Money

$5.00		$2.00	$1.00	25¢	10¢	5¢	1¢

Circle the money that adds up to the amount in the box.

Estimate how much money each child has. Write your estimate on the line.
Count the actual amount. Write it on the line.

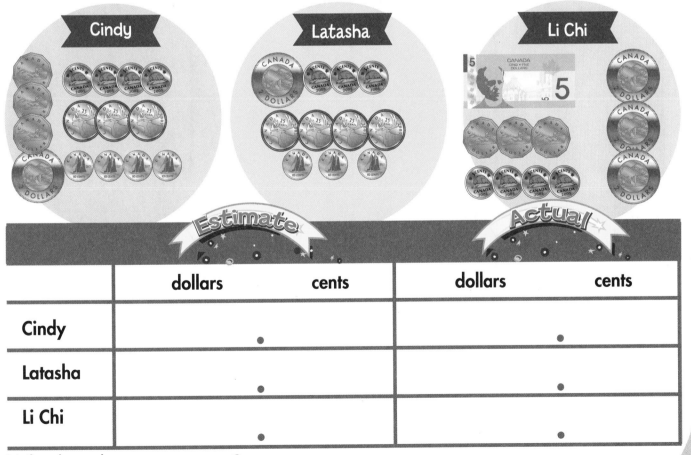

	Estimate		**Actual**	
	dollars	cents	dollars	cents
Cindy				
Latasha				
Li Chi				

Who has the most money? _____
Who has the least money? _____

Canadian Money

$5.00　　　　$2.00　$1.00　25¢　10¢　5¢　1¢

Draw the fewest coins and bills you could use to pay for each item.

| $5.45 | $0.89 | $3.67 | $7.92 |

Shawn has $9.64

Robert has $1.36 less money than Shawn.

How much money does Robert have? _____

Length

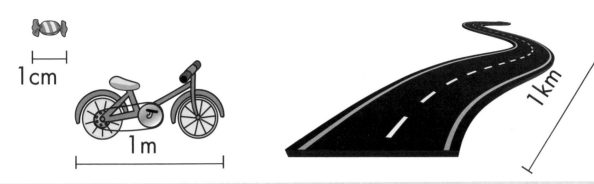

What units are the best to do these measurements?
Print km, m, or cm on the lines.

m

_____

_____

_____

_____

_____

_____

Measurement

Length Answer the questions using km, m , or cm.

How tall is the Prime Minister? About 2 _____ .

How long is your shoe? About 15 _____ .

How far is it from Calgary to Toronto? About 2 000 _____ .

How long is your dad's arm? About 1 _____ .

How tall is an apple? About 6 _____ .

Measure each line. Record the length in the box.
Don't forget to include the units.

14 cm

Length

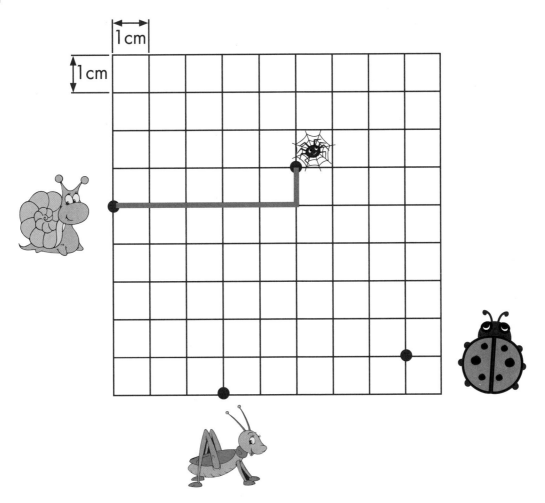

Using **green**, follow the lines to draw the route from the snail to the spider. How long is the route? ____6____ cm

Using **blue**, follow the lines to show the route from the spider to the cricket. How long is the route? _____ cm

Using **red**, follow the lines to draw the route from the ladybug to the snail. _____ cm

How far is it all together from the cricket to the lady bug, then to the spider, then to the snail, and back to the cricket? _____ cm
Draw the route **purple**.

Time

When telling time, the short hand tells the hour and the long hand tells the minutes.

Skip count by 5 to count the minutes.
Start at 12.

Write the time shown to the nearest 5 minutes.

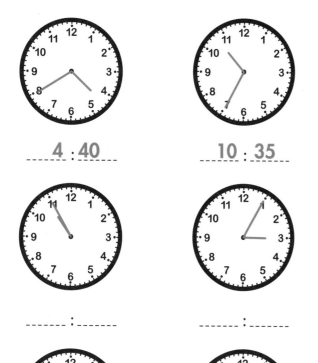

4 : 40   10 : 35   8 : 20   10 : 35

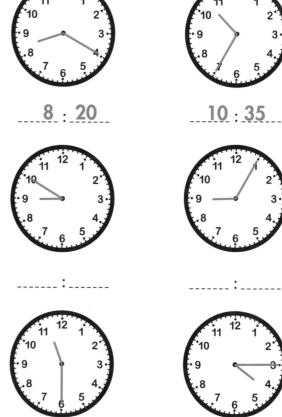

_____ : _____   _____ : _____   _____ : _____   _____ : _____

__5__ minutes after __2__   _____ minutes before _____   _____ minutes before _____   _____ minutes after _____
                                                                       _____ minutes after _____

Draw the hands to match the time on the digital clock.

         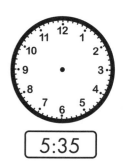

| 9:05 | | 12:50 | | 2:10 | | 5:35 |

Measurement

Time Maze
Draw the hands on the clocks from start to end.

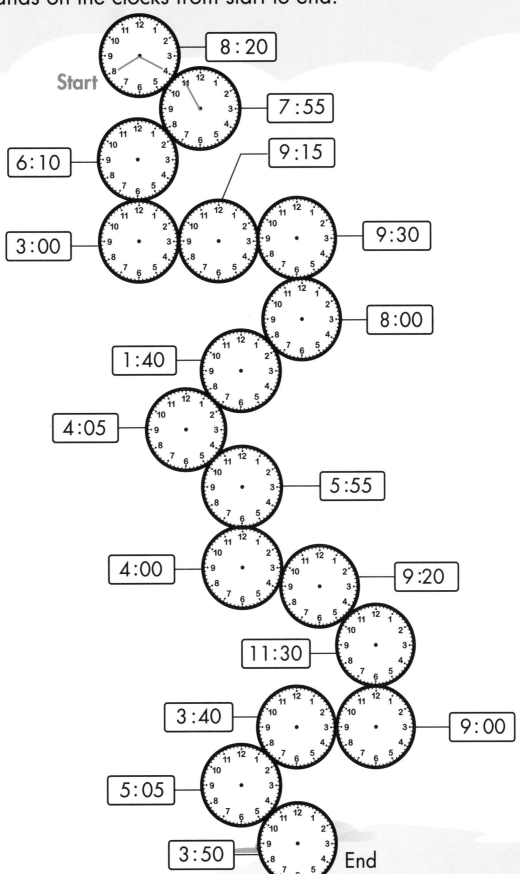

Start

8 : 20

7 : 55

6 : 10

9 : 15

3 : 00

9 : 30

8 : 00

1 : 40

4 : 05

5 : 55

4 : 00

9 : 20

11 : 30

3 : 40

9 : 00

5 : 05

3 : 50

End

Temperature

We measure temperature with a thermometer. We tell the temperature using degrees Celcius (°C).

Write the temperature.

____ °C   ____ °C   ____ °C

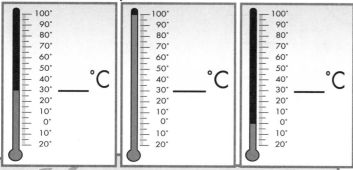

HOT and COLD

Water turns to ice at 0°. It is cold.

0°C

Water boils at 100°. It is hot.

100°C

A nice warm day at the beach is 25°C. It is warm.

25°C

What temperature is it?

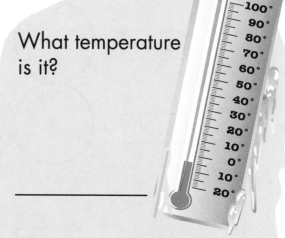

_____

Circle the things that you need for this tempertaure.

Circle the correct temperature.

100° C
25° C
0° C

100° C
25° C
0° C

100° C
25° C
0° C

Measurement

Capacity

Capacity tells how much a container can hold. Millilitres (ml) and litres (L) are units for measuring capacity. One ml is smaller than an eraser. One L is about the amount in a water bottle.

What is the capacity of each container? Circle the answers. Some are done.

(less than 1L)
about 1L
more than 1L

less than 1L
about 1L
(more than 1L)

less than 1L
(about 1L)
more than 1L

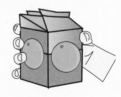

less than 1L
about 1L
more than 1L

less than 1L
about 1L
more than 1L

less than 1L
about 1L
more than 1L

Draw the amount of grape juice in each container.

Draw 2L.

3L
2L
1L

Draw 3L.

4L
3L
2L
1L

Draw 4L.

5L
4L
3L
2L
1L

Draw 8L.

9L
8L
7L
6L
5L
4L
3L
2L
1L

Capacity

What is the capacity of each container? Circle the answer.

about 50 L
more than 200 L

less than 1 L
about 10 L

less than 1L
about 10 L

Answer the questions.

How many pails full of water will fill the tub? _____

250ml

How many glasses can be filled from the full pitcher? _____

Hint: 1000 ml is 1 L
        2000 ml is 2 L

How much juice is in each container?
Use these words: a quarter of a litre, half a litre, three quarters of a litre

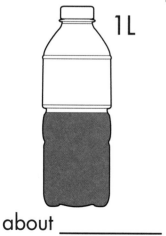

1L

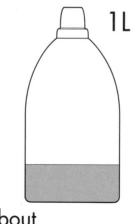

1L

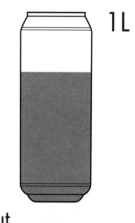

1L

about _____

about _____

about _____

Measurement

Mass

Mass tells the amount of substance in a thing.
Grams (g) and kilograms (kg) are units for measuring mass.
What is the mass of each object? Write it on the line. Two examples are done.

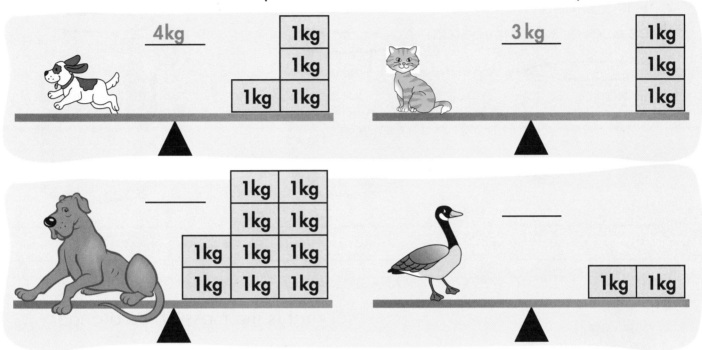

Draw the number of 1kg needed to balance the scales.

How many 1kg need to be added to the goose to equal the mass of the big dog?

Mass

What is the mass of the grape jelly in each container?
Use these words:

    a quarter of a kilogram
    a half a kilogram
    three-quarters of a kilogram

_____

_____

  _____

_____

_____

  _____

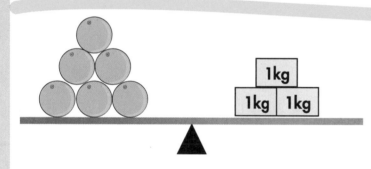

What is the mass of the oranges?

_____

What is the mass of one orange?

_____

What is the mass of 12 oranges?

_____

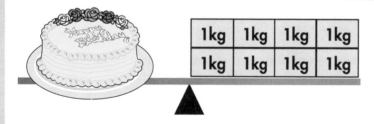

What is the mass of the cake? _____

What is the mass of half of the cake? _____

What is the mass of a quarter of the cake? _____

3-D Shapes

cube   sphere   cylinder   cone   rectangular prism

Colour the sphere shapes red.

Colour the cube shapes blue.

Colour the cylinder shapes green.

Colour the cone shapes orange.

Colour the rectangular prism shapes purple.

Polygons

A **polygon** is a 2-D (flat) shape with 3 or more **sides** made of straight lines. Here are 5 kinds of polygons.

 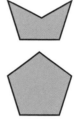 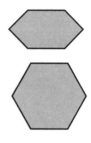 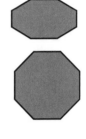

triangle	quadrilateral	pentagon	hexagon	octagon
• 3 sides	• 4 sides	• 5 sides	• 6 sides	• 8 sides

Print the name of each polygon on the line below the shape. Then colour it to match the categories above.

  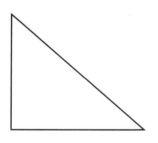

quadrilateral
_____

_____

_____

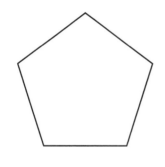 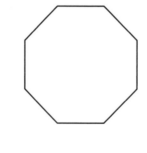 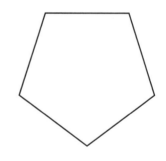

_____

_____

_____

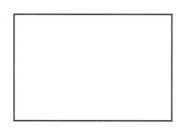 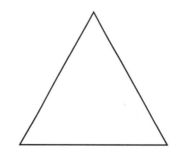 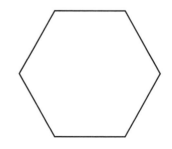

_____

_____

_____

Polygons

A **polygon** has 3 or more straight **sides** or **edges**. The sides meet at the **vertices** (or **corners**). A single corner is called a **vertex**.

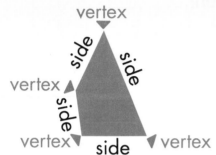

This polygon has 4 vertices and 4 sides.

Fill in the number of sides and vertices for each polygon.

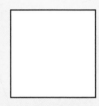
- ___4___ sides
- ___4___ vertices

- _____ sides
- _____ vertices

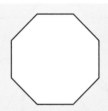
- _____ sides
- _____ vertices

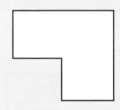
- _____ sides
- _____ vertices

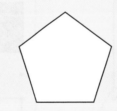
- _____ sides
- _____ vertices

- _____ sides
- _____ vertices

Review:

triangle: _____ sides
_____ vertices

square: _____ sides
_____ vertices

octagon: _____ sides
_____ vertices

pentagon: _____ sides
_____ vertices

hexagon: _____ sides
_____ vertices

rectangle: _____ sides
_____ vertices

Symmetry

Some shapes have **lines of symmetry**. That means if the shape is cut in half each side is the mirror image of the other. You can check for symmetry by cutting the shape out and folding it. If the halves match exactly, the fold shows a line of symmetry. We say the shape is **symmetrical**.

The dotted line is the line of symmetry.

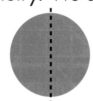

The dotted line is **not** the line of symmetry.

Circle the pictures where the dotted line shows the line of symmetry. Put an X on those where it does not.

   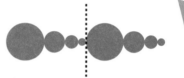

Draw a line of symmetry on each shape. They each have more than one.

 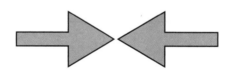 

Make the picture symmetrical by adding what is missing.

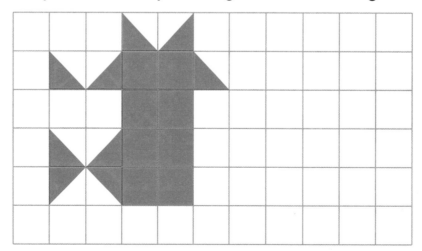

Prisms

A **prism** is a 3-D shape that has 2 **bases** that are the same, and **sides that are rectangles**. We identify a prism by its base shape.

Shape of bases: triangles
Prism name: triangular prism

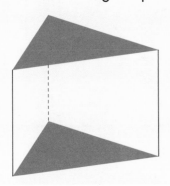

Shape of bases: rectangles
Prism name: rectangular prism

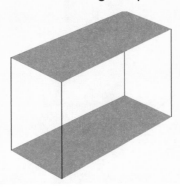

Shape of bases: pentagons
Prism name: pentagonal prism

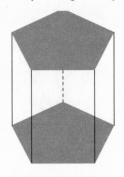

Identify these prisms by their base shape.

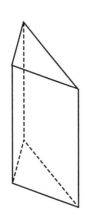

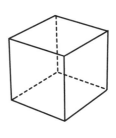

Shape of bases: _____

Prism name:_____

Shape of bases: _____

Prism name:_____

Shape of bases: _____

Prism name:_____

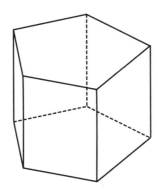

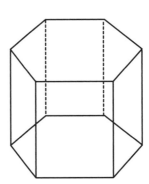

Shape of bases: _____

Prism name:_____

Shape of bases: _____

Prism name:_____

Pyramids

Pyramids have **1 base** and **sides that are triangular** which meet at the top. Pyramids are identified by their bases.

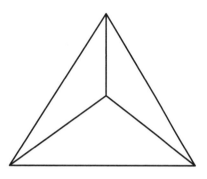

triangular pyramid

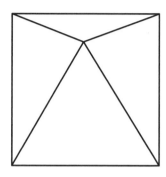

square pyramid

Colour the base of each pyramid.
Write the shape of the base on the line.

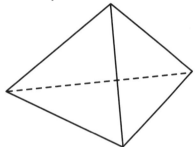

Shape of base: _____

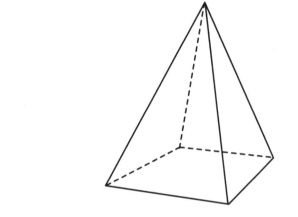

Shape of base: _____

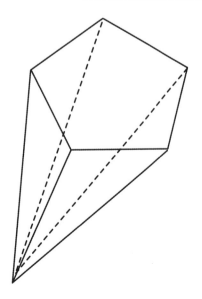

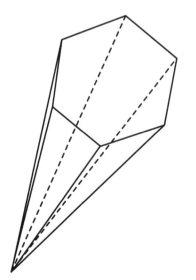

Shape of base: _____   Shape of base: _____

Prisms and Pyramids

Faces are the flat surfaces of a 3-D shape. Count the faces and edges on each shape. Record the numbers. Then circle the vertices. Count and record the numbers. Then colour the **prisms red** and the **pyramids blue**.

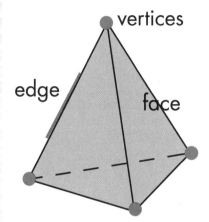

vertices

edge   face

__4__ faces

__6__ edges

__4__ vertices

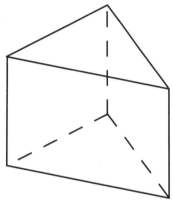

_____ faces

_____ edges

_____ vertices

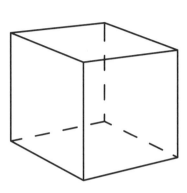

_____ faces

_____ edges

_____ vertices

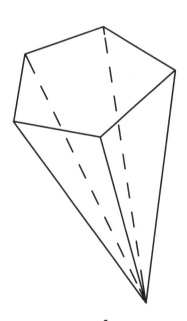

_____ faces

_____ edges

_____ vertices

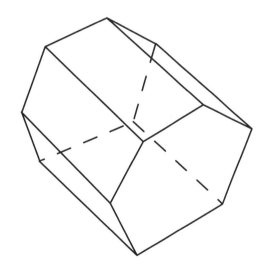

_____ faces

_____ edges

_____ vertices

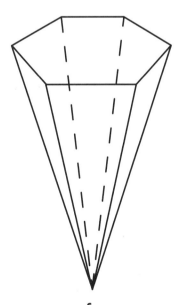

_____ faces

_____ edges

_____ vertices

Geometry and Spatial Sense

Location and Movement
Look at the grid map. Fill in the blanks.

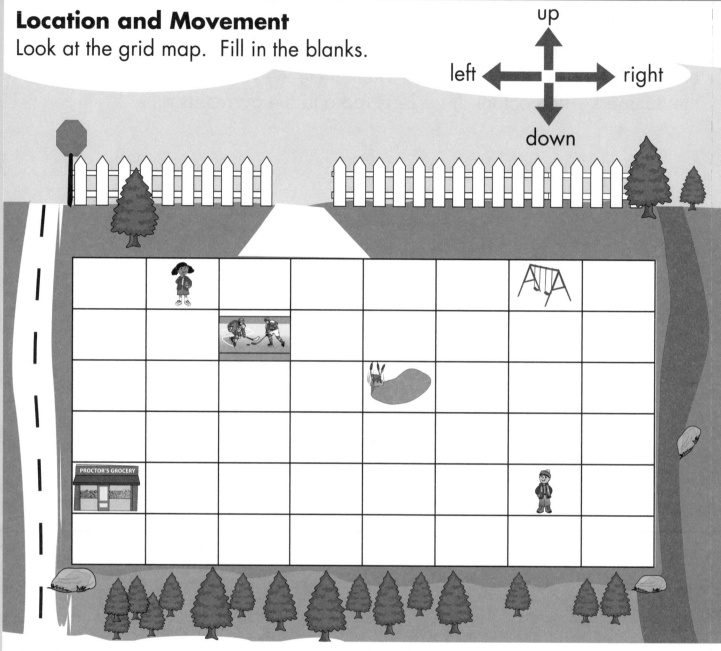

The skating rink is _____ squares to the left of the river.

The swing is _____ squares up from the trees.

The pond is _____ squares to the right of the road.

The store is _____ squares down from the fence.

Joe is _____squares to the right of the store and _____ squares to the left of the river.

Jill is _____squares to the right of the road and _____ squares to the left of the swing.

Geometry and Spatial Sense

Location and Movement

Follow the instructions to move each item on the grid. Draw a line from square to square to the new location. Then draw the item in its new location.

 4 squares to the right and 1 square up.

 2 squares down and 5 squares left.

 2 squares to the right and 1 square down.

 3 squares to the left and 1 squares down.

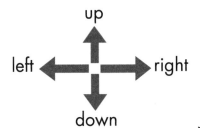

up

left ← → right

down

Location and Movement
Look at the grid. Answer the questions.

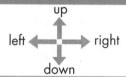

Draw the shortest path from the grocery store to the post office. Describe it below.

_____

Draw the shortest path from the park to the hospital. Describe it below.

_____

Draw the shortest path from the park to the bookstore. Describe it below.

_____

Draw the shortest path from the post office to the school. Describe it below.

Patterns

Look at each pattern. Draw and colour the next three shapes.

Growing and Shrinking Patterns

A **growing** pattern gets larger every time.

A **shrinking** pattern gets smaller every time.

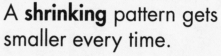
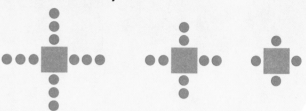

Fill in the blanks in the patterns.

The pattern is _____growing_____.

The pattern is _____.

The pattern is _____.

2   4   ____   ____   10   ____   ____   ____

The pattern is _____.

55   50   45   ____   ____   30   ____   ____   ____

The pattern is _____.

Patterning Rules
Number patterns can be created by adding and/or subtracting numbers.

Create a number pattern by following the pattern rule.

Pattern rule: Add 4 each time.

0   _4_   _8_   ___   ___   ___   ___   ___   ___

Add 3 each time.
15   ___   ___   ___   ___   ___   ___   ___   ___

Subtract 4 each time.
64   ___   ___   ___   ___   ___   ___   ___   ___

Subtract 5 each time.
50   ___   ___   ___   ___   ___   ___   ___   ___

Follow the instructions to make patterns.

Start at 36. Make a number pattern that extends by adding 8 each time.

___   ___   ___   ___   ___   ___   ___

Start at 64. Make a number pattern that extends by subtracting 4 each time.

___   ___   ___   ___   ___   ___   ___

Fact Families

Look at each pair of number sentences. Find the missing number.

$11 - 4 = 7$
$4 + \underline{\ 7\ } = 11$

$13 + 16 = 29$
$29 - \underline{\ \ \ } = 16$

$16 + 23 = 39$
$\underline{\ \ \ } - 23 = 16$

$14 - 7 = 7$
$7 + \underline{\ 7\ } = 14$

$5 + 15 = 20$
$20 - \underline{\ \ \ } = 5$

$42 - 12 = 30$
$\underline{\ \ \ } + 30 = 42$

Beside each number sentence, write another number sentence in the same fact family. There are two possible answers.

$31 + 6 = 37$ $\quad\underline{37 - 31 = 6 \qquad 37 - 6 = 31}$

$5 + 6 = 11$ $\quad\underline{\hspace{5cm}}$

$19 + 7 = 26$ $\quad\underline{\hspace{5cm}}$

$12 + 5 = 17$ $\quad\underline{\hspace{5cm}}$

$22 - 16 = 6$ $\quad\underline{\hspace{5cm}}$

$8 + 7 = 15$ $\quad\underline{\hspace{5cm}}$

$24 - 5 = 19$ $\quad\underline{\hspace{5cm}}$

$22 - 18 = 4$ $\quad\underline{\hspace{5cm}}$

$5 + 14 = 19$ $\quad\underline{\hspace{5cm}}$

$9 + 5 = 14$ $\quad\underline{\hspace{5cm}}$

$37 - 13 = 24$ $\quad\underline{\hspace{5cm}}$

$35 - 28 = 7$ $\quad\underline{\hspace{5cm}}$

Fact Families Challenge: Equations

Remember that whatever is on one side of an = must be equal to what is on the other side. This is called an equation.

Try this challenge: Find the missing number in each equation. Use fact families to help.

Hint: First simplify the equation by solving the complete side of the equation.

Example:

$12 + 3 = \boxed{} - 6$

The complete side of the equation is 12 + 3. That adds up to 15, so

$15 = \boxed{} - 6$

If $\boxed{} - 6 = 15$, then by thinking of this fact family we know that

$15 + 6 = \boxed{}$

Now add the complete side of the equation to find the answer.

$15 + 6 = 21$

$\boxed{} = 21$

Simplify the equations below. Then solve them using fact families to help you. The first one gives hints.

$25 - 6 = \boxed{} + 14$

Simplify 25 – 6 and write the answer where the $\boxed{}$ is below.

$\boxed{} = \boxed{} + 14$

Now use the fact family help you.

Write the number again in the $\boxed{}$ below.

$\boxed{} - 14 = \boxed{}$

Now subtract to find the answer.

$\boxed{} =$

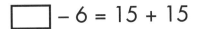

$\boxed{} - 6 = 15 + 15$

$\boxed{} - 6 = \boxed{}$

$\boxed{} + 6 = \boxed{}$

$\boxed{} =$

Graphs

Read the graph and answer the questions.

Thirty students in Ms. Kenny's class did a survey to find out what their favourite type of healthy snack was. This graph shows their data.

Favourite Snacks in Ms. Kenny's Class

fruit	
granola	
vegetables	
cheese and crackers	

Each picture represents _____ students.

1. If there are 30 students in Ms. Kenny's class, how many students does each piece of food represent? _____

_____

2. What was the most popular snack? _____

3. What was the least popular snack? _____

4. How many people liked fruit best? _____

5. How many people liked granola best? _____

6. How many people liked vegetables best? _____

7. How many people liked cheese and crackers best? _____

8. What is your favourite type of healthy snack? _____

Graphs

The graph below is called a **bar graph**.
Read the graph and answer the questions.

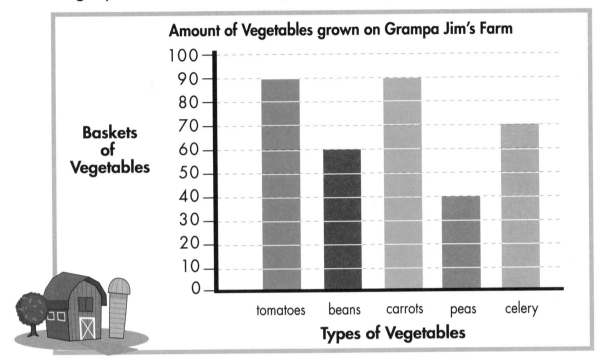

1. What does the graph tell us about? _____

_____

2. How many baskets of tomatoes does Grampa Jim grow? _____

_____

3. How many more beans than peas does he grow? _____

_____

4. What does Grampa Jim grow the most of? _____

_____

5. What does Grampa Jim grow the least of? _____

_____

6. How many types of vegetables does Grampa Jim grow? _____

_____

7. How many baskets of vegetables does Grampa Jim grow all together? _____

_____

Graphs

Mr. Milgram has 5 bakeries. He kept track of how long it took each bakery to sell 5 apple pies. Fill in the blanks and put the data in the graph. Then answer the questions. Look at the previous page for help.

Bakery	Number of Days to Sell 5 Pies
A	5
B	25
C	15
D	10
E	20

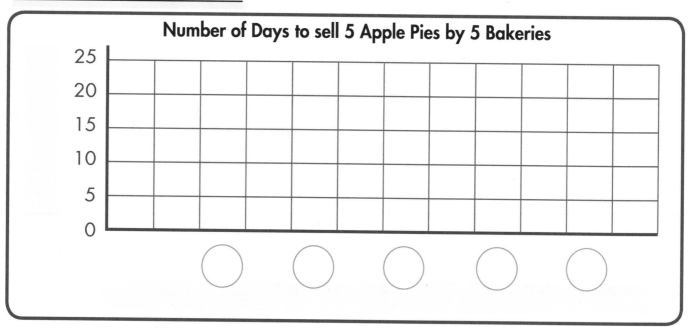

Number of Days to sell 5 Apple Pies by 5 Bakeries

What is the title of the graph?_____

How many days does each square represent? _____ days.

How many bakeries took more than 2 weeks to sell 5 apple pies?

_____bakeries.

Which bakery sold 5 apple pies in the shortest time? _____

Which bakery sold 5 apple pies in less than 2 weeks? _____

Graphs

Natasha is baking giant cookies for her school's bake sale. She is baking several different kinds of cookies.

Fill in the blanks and put the data in the horizontal bar graph.

Type of Cookie	Number
chocolate chip	24
oatmeal chocolate chip	18
sugar cookie	12
shortbread	12
gingerbread	18

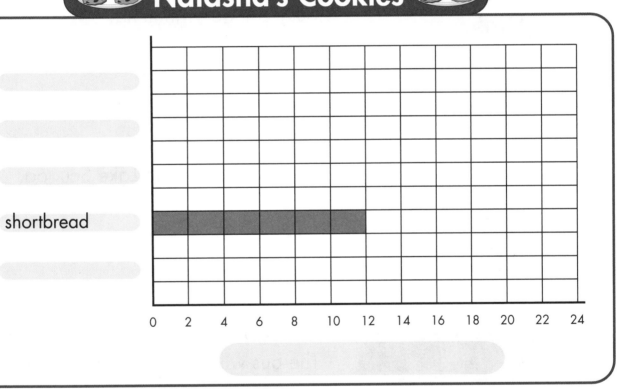

Natasha's Cookies

shortbread

0 2 4 6 8 10 12 14 16 18 20 22 24

How many different kinds of cookies is she baking? _____ kinds

How many different types of cookies have chocolate chips? _____ cookies

How many cookies has she made in all? _____ cookies

If each cookie cost $1, how much will be collected from selling

all the cookies? $_____

Probability

How likely is each event?
Print the answer on the line.
Use the words here: **impossible**, **unlikely**, **likely**, or **certain**.

 The bee will return to the hive to make honey.

_____

 Susy will go swimming.

_____

 Jimmy will canoe in Lake Scugog.

_____

 The bus will fit in my single car garage.

_____

The fire truck will put out the fire.

 _____

50

Data Management and Probability

Probability is the chance that a certain outcome will occur.

If you flip a coin the probability that it will land on heads is 1 for every 2 times thrown.

Look at the blocks in the box. If you take one block out 20 times in a row. without looking, how many times will you take out each type of block? Circle the best prediction.

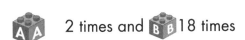 2 times and 18 times

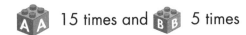 15 times and 5 times

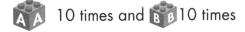 10 times and 10 times

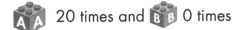 20 times and 0 times

Look at the marbles in a bowl. If you take one marble out 40 times in a row without looking, how many times will you take out each colour marble? Circle the best prediction.

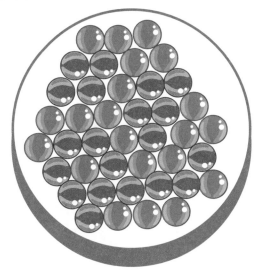

40 times and 0 times

18 times and 22 times

7 times and 33 times

30 times and 10 times

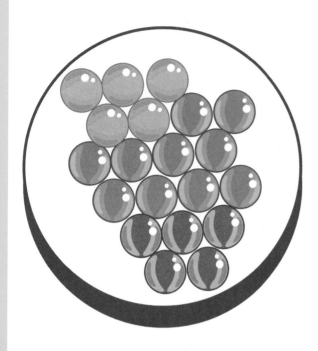

Take one marble from the bowl.
What are the possible outcomes?

_____

Are the chances of taking a 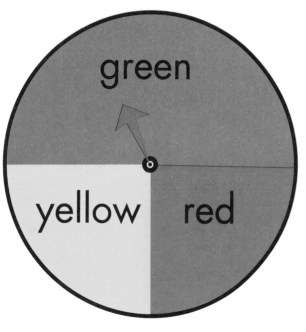 or a the same? _____

_____

Are the chances of taking a or a the same? _____

_____

_____

If you take out a marble 40 times without looking, how many times will you take out each colour marble? Put your prediction on the line.

      _____ times

      _____ times

      _____ times

Spin the arrow once. What are the possible outcomes?

_____

If you spin the arrow 40 times without looking, how many times do you predict it will land on each colour?

Green _____ times
Yellow _____ times
Red _____ time

Think about it:

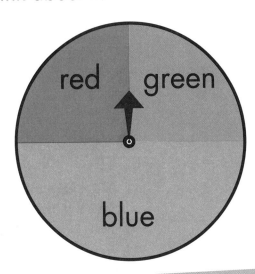

What is the probability that the spinner will land on yellow? **Impossible**

Is it more likely for the spinner to land on red or green? **It is equally likely because the red and green section are equal size.**

Is it impossible, unlikely, likely, or certain that the spinner will land on blue? **It is likely because blue is the largest section.**

Read the descriptions and colour the spinners to match.

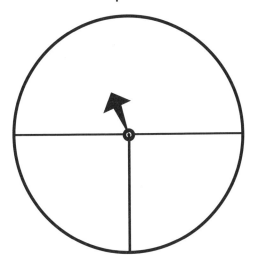

It is equally likely for the spinner to land on purple or green.

It is likely for the spinner to land on red.

It is impossible for the spinner to land on blue.

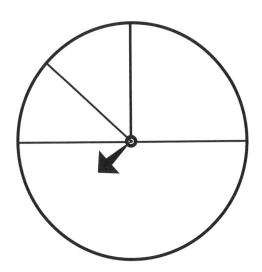

It is equally likely for the spinner to land on yellow or green.

It is more likely for the spinner to land on red than purple.

Think about it: Circle the words to finish the sentences:

Example:

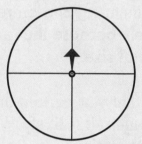

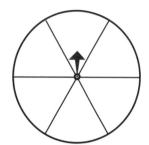

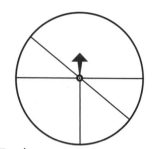

Each outcome is **equally likely**.
The sections are **congruent**.
The spinner is **fair**.

Each outcome
    is equally likely.
    is not equally likely.
These sections are
    congruent incongruent
The spinner is **fair unfair.**

Each outcome
    is equally likely.
    is not equally likely.
These sections are
    congruent incongruent
The spinner is **fair unfair.**

Circle the correct word to complete the sentences.
This spinner has 8 **congruent**
                incongruent sections.

Answer the questions.

Out of 8 sections, how many sections say "win"? _____

Out of 8 sections, how many sections say "lose"? _____

Out of 8 sections, how many sections say "try again"? _____

What is the probability of each outcome?
Win   ____ in ____
Lose   ____ in ____
Try again   ____ in ____

Is the spinner fair?   Yes   No

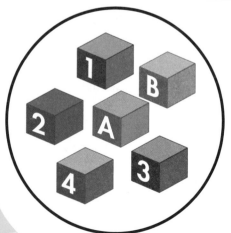

If you take one block out without looking, what is the probability of each outcome?

A   ____ in ____
A number   ____ in ____
A letter   ____ in ____
An even number   ____ in ____

Venn Diagrams

A Venn diagram represents sets using circles. Where the circles intersect, the items are included in both circles.

Children Who Play Soccer   Children Who Practice Karate

Nine children were surveyed to find out if they played soccer, practiced karate, or both. Look at the Venn diagram to answer the following questions.

How many children play soccer? _____

How many children practice karate? _____

How many children play soccer and practice karate? _____

What activity do Amir and Kate have in common? _____

How many children play soccer but do not practice karate?_____

How many children practice karate but do not play soccer? _____

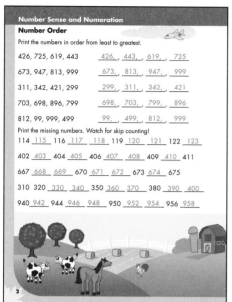

Page 2

Number Sense and Numeration

Number Order

Print the numbers in order from least to greatest.

426, 725, 619, 443   _426_, _443_, _619_, _725_

673, 947, 813, 999   _673_, _813_, _947_, _999_

311, 342, 421, 299   _299_, _311_, _342_, _421_

703, 698, 896, 799   _698_, _703_, _799_, _896_

812, 99, 999, 499   _99_, _499_, _812_, _999_

Print the missing numbers. Watch for skip counting!

114 _115_ 116 _117_ _118_ 119 _120_ _121_ 122 _123_

402 _403_ 404 _405_ 406 _407_ _408_ 409 _410_ 411

667 _668_ _669_ 670 _671_ _672_ 673 _674_ 675

310 320 _330_ _340_ 350 _360_ _370_ 380 _390_ _400_

940 _942_ 944 _946_ 948 950 _952_ _954_ 956 _958_

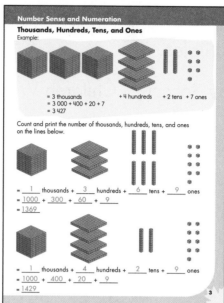

Page 3

Number Sense and Numeration

Thousands, Hundreds, Tens, and Ones

Example:

= 3 thousands   + 4 hundreds   + 2 tens   + 7 ones
= 3 000 + 400 + 20 + 7
= 3 427

Count and print the number of thousands, hundreds, tens, and ones on the lines below.

= _1_ thousands + _3_ hundreds + _6_ tens + _9_ ones
= _1000_ + _300_ + _60_ + _9_
= _1369_

= _1_ thousands + _4_ hundreds + _2_ tens + _9_ ones
= _1000_ + _400_ + _20_ + _9_
= _1429_

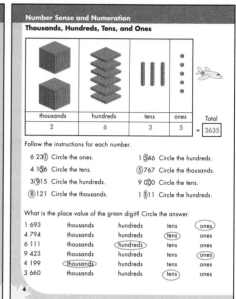

Page 4

Number Sense and Numeration

Thousands, Hundreds, Tens, and Ones

thousands	hundreds	tens	ones	Total
2	6	3	5	= 2635

Follow the instructions for each number.

6 23① Circle the ones.   1 ⑤46 Circle the hundreds.
4 1⑤6 Circle the tens.   ⑤767 Circle the thousands.
3⑨15 Circle the hundreds.   9 0⓪0 Circle the tens.
⑧121 Circle the thousands.   1 ①11 Circle the hundreds.

What is the place value of the green digit? Circle the answer.

1 693	thousands	hundreds	tens	(ones)
4 794	thousands	hundreds	(tens)	ones
6 111	thousands	(hundreds)	tens	ones
9 423	thousands	hundreds	tens	(ones)
4 199	(thousands)	hundreds	tens	ones
3 660	thousands	hundreds	(tens)	ones

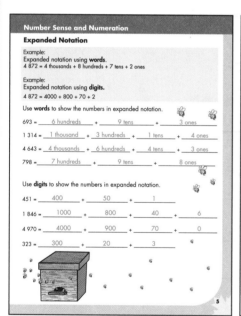

Page 5

Number Sense and Numeration

Expanded Notation

Example:
Expanded notation using **words**.
4 872 = 4 thousands + 8 hundreds + 7 tens + 2 ones

Example:
Expanded notation using **digits**.
4 872 = 4000 + 800 + 70 + 2

Use **words** to show the numbers in expanded notation.

693 = _6 hundreds_ + _9 tens_ + _3 ones_

1 314 = _1 thousand_ + _3 hundreds_ + _1 tens_ + _4 ones_

4 643 = _4 thousands_ + _6 hundreds_ + _4 tens_ + _3 ones_

798 = _7 hundreds_ + _9 tens_ + _8 ones_

Use **digits** to show the numbers in expanded notation.

451 = _400_ + _50_ + _1_

1 846 = _1000_ + _800_ + _40_ + _6_

4 970 = _4000_ + _900_ + _70_ + _0_

323 = _300_ + _20_ + _3_

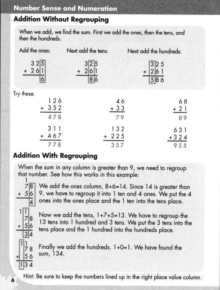

Page 6

Number Sense and Numeration

Addition Without Regrouping

When we add, we find the sum. First we add the ones, then the tens, and then the hundreds.

Add the ones: Next add the tens: Next add the hundreds:

```
  325            325              325
+ 261          + 261            + 261
    6             86              586
```

Try these.

```
  126            46              68
+ 352          + 33           + 21
  478            79              89

  311           132             631
+ 467          + 225          + 324
  778            357             955
```

Addition With Regrouping

When the sum in any column is greater than 9, we need to regroup that number. See how this works in this example:

```
  1
  78    We add the ones column, 8+6=14. Since 14 is greater than
+ 56    9, we have to regroup it into 1 ten and 4 ones. We put the 4
   4    ones into the ones place and the 1 ten into the tens place.
```

```
 11
 78     Now we add the tens, 1+7+5=13. We have to regroup the
+56     13 tens into 1 hundred and 3 tens. We put the 3 tens into the
 34     tens place and the 1 hundred into the hundreds place.
```

```
 11
 78     Finally we add the hundreds. 1+0=1. We have found the
+56     sum, 134.
134
```

Hint: Be sure to keep the numbers lined up in the right place value column.

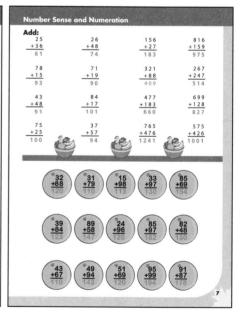

Page 7

Number Sense and Numeration

Add:

```
  25        26       156      816
+ 36      + 48      + 27    + 159
  61        74       183      975

  78        71       321      267
+ 15      + 19      + 88    + 247
  93        90       409      514

  43        84       477      699
+ 48      + 17      + 183   + 128
  91       101       660      827

  75        37       765      575
+ 25      + 57      + 476   + 426
 100        94      1241     1001
```

① 32   ② 31   ③ 15   ④ 33   ⑤ 85
 +88   +79   +98   +97   +69
 120   110   113   130   154

⑥ 39   ⑦ 89   ⑧ 24   ⑨ 85   ⑩ 82
 +84   +58   +96   +97   +48
 123   147   120   182   130

⑪ 43   ⑫ 49   ⑬ 51   ⑭ 95   ⑮ 91
 +67   +94   +69   +99   +87
 110   143   120   194   178

Solutions

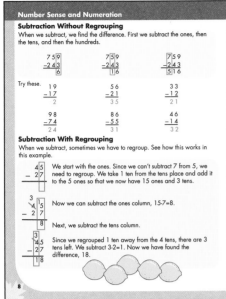

Number Sense and Numeration

Subtraction Without Regrouping

When we subtract, we find the difference. First we subtract the ones, then the tens, and then the hundreds.

```
7 5 9        7 5 9        7 5 9
-2 4 3       -2 4 3       -2 4 3
    6          1 6        5 1 6
```

Try these.
```
 1 9         5 6          3 3
-1 7        -2 1         -1 2
   2          3 5          2 1

 9 8         8 6          4 6
-7 4        -5 5         -1 4
 2 4          3 1          3 2
```

Subtraction With Regrouping

When we subtract, sometimes we have to regroup. See how this works in this example.

```
 4 5
-2 7
```
We start with the ones. Since we can't subtract 7 from 5, we need to regroup. We take 1 ten from the tens place and add it to the 5 ones so that we now have 15 ones and 3 tens.

```
 3
 4 15
-2 7
    8
```
Now we can subtract the ones column, 15-7=8.

Next, we subtract the tens column.

```
 3
 4 15
-2 7
 1 8
```
Since we regrouped 1 ten away from the 4 tens, there are 3 tens left. We subtract 3-2=1. Now we have found the difference, 18.

Page 8

Number Sense and Numeration

Subtract:

```
1. 355      4. 186      7. 618     10. 378
  -143        -169        -332        -298
   212          17         286          80

2. 725      5. 890      8. 644     11. 467
  -412        -271        -427        -121
   313         619         217         346

3. 967      6. 579      9. 399     12. 471
  -132        -176        -386        -330
   835         403          13         141
```

Page 9

Number Sense and Numeration

Subtraction

Add and subtract to solve the word problems.

Jeff has 363 hockey cards and Jake has 193 hockey cards.

a. How many hockey cards do the boys have in all?

___556___ hockey cards
363+193=556

b. How many more hockey cards does Jeff have than Jake?

___170___ more
```
 363
-193
 170
```

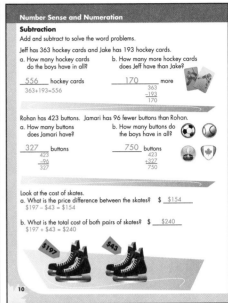

Rohan has 423 buttons. Jamari has 96 fewer buttons than Rohan.

a. How many buttons does Jamari have?

___327___ buttons
```
 423
- 96
 327
```

b. How many buttons do the boys have in all?

___750___ buttons
```
 423
+327
 750
```

Look at the cost of skates.

a. What is the price difference between the skates? $ ___154___
$197 – $43 = $154

b. What is the total cost of both pairs of skates? $ ___240___
$197 + $43 = $240

Page 10

Number Sense and Numeration

Multiplication

Multiplication is a way to add numbers faster. Multiplication is adding the same number together multiple times. When numbers are multiplied, the answer is called the product.

Example:

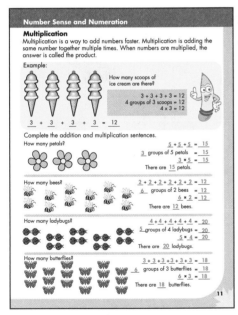

How many scoops of ice cream are there?
```
3 + 3 + 3 + 3 = 12
4 groups of 3 scoops = 12
4 × 3 = 12
```

```
3 + 3 + 3 + 3 = 12
```

Complete the addition and multiplication sentences.

How many petals?
```
5 + 5 + 5 = 15
3 groups of 5 petals = 15
3 × 5 = 15
There are 15 petals.
```

How many bees?
```
2 + 2 + 2 + 2 + 2 + 2 = 12
6 groups of 2 bees = 12
6 × 2 = 12
There are 12 bees.
```

How many ladybugs?
```
4 + 4 + 4 + 4 + 4 = 20
5 groups of 4 ladybugs = 20
5 × 4 = 20
There are 20 ladybugs.
```

How many butterflies?
```
3 + 3 + 3 + 3 + 3 + 3 = 18
6 groups of 3 butterflies = 18
6 × 3 = 18
There are 18 butterflies.
```

Page 11

Number Sense and Numeration

Multiplication

Look at the pictures. Fill in the blanks.

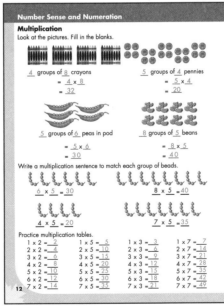

__4__ groups of __8__ crayons
```
= 4 × 8
= 32
```

__5__ groups of __4__ pennies
```
= 5 × 4
= 20
```

__5__ groups of __6__ peas in pod
```
= 5 × 6
= 30
```

__8__ groups of __5__ beans
```
= 8 × 5
= 40
```

Write a multiplication sentence to match each group of beads.

```
6 × 5 = 30                    8 × 5 = 40

4 × 5 = 20                    7 × 5 = 35
```

Practice multiplication tables.

1 × 2 = 2	1 × 5 = 5	1 × 3 = 3	1 × 7 = 7
2 × 2 = 4	2 × 5 = 10	2 × 3 = 6	2 × 7 = 14
3 × 2 = 6	3 × 5 = 15	3 × 3 = 9	3 × 7 = 21
4 × 2 = 8	4 × 5 = 20	4 × 3 = 12	4 × 7 = 28
5 × 2 = 10	5 × 5 = 25	5 × 3 = 15	5 × 7 = 35
6 × 2 = 12	6 × 5 = 30	6 × 3 = 18	6 × 7 = 42
7 × 2 = 14	7 × 5 = 35	7 × 3 = 21	7 × 7 = 49

Page 12

Number Sense and Numeration

Division

Division is equal sharing or grouping. The answer to the question is called a quotient.

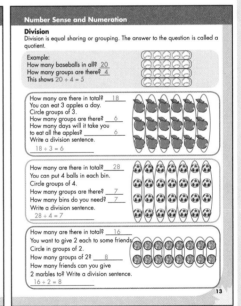

Example:
How many baseballs in all? __20__
How many groups are there? __4__
This shows 20 ÷ 4 = 5

How many are there in total? __18__
You can eat 3 apples a day.
Circle groups of 3.
How many groups are there? __6__
How many days will it take you to eat all the apples? __6__
Write a division sentence.
```
18 ÷ 3 = 6
```

How many are there in total? __28__
You can put 4 balls in each bin.
Circle groups of 4.
How many groups are there? __7__
How many bins do you need? __7__
Write a division sentence.
```
28 ÷ 4 = 7
```

How many are there in total? __16__
You want to give 2 each to some friends.
Circle in groups of 2.
How many groups of 2? __8__
How many friends can you give 2 marbles to? Write a division sentence.
```
16 ÷ 2 = 8
```

Page 13

Solutions

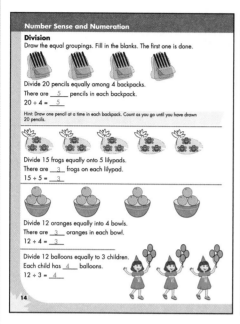

Number Sense and Numeration

Division

Draw the equal groupings. Fill in the blanks. The first one is done.

Divide 20 pencils equally among 4 backpacks.
There are __5__ pencils in each backpack.
20 ÷ 4 = __5__

Hint: Draw one pencil at a time in each backpack. Count as you go until you have drawn 20 pencils.

Divide 15 frogs equally onto 5 lilypads.
There are __3__ frogs on each lilypad.
15 ÷ 5 = __3__

Divide 12 oranges equally into 4 bowls.
There are __3__ oranges in each bowl.
12 ÷ 4 = __3__

Divide 12 balloons equally to 3 children.
Each child has __4__ balloons.
12 ÷ 3 = __4__

Page 14

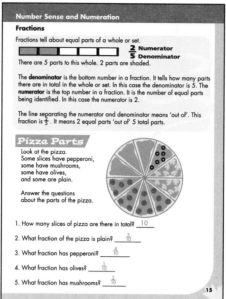

Number Sense and Numeration

Fractions

Fractions tell about equal parts of a whole or set.

2 Numerator
5 Denominator

There are 5 parts to this whole. 2 parts are shaded.

The **denominator** is the bottom number in a fraction. It tells how many parts there are in total in the whole or set. In this case the denominator is 5. The **numerator** is the top number in a fraction. It is the number of equal parts being identified. In this case the numerator is 2.

The line separating the numerator and denominator means 'out of'. This fraction is $\frac{2}{5}$. It means 2 equal parts 'out of' 5 total parts.

Pizza Parts

Look at the pizza.
Some slices have pepperoni, some have mushrooms, some have olives, and some are plain.

Answer the questions about the parts of the pizza.

1. How many slices of pizza are there in total? __10__
2. What fraction of the pizza is plain? $\frac{2}{10}$
3. What fraction has pepperoni? $\frac{4}{10}$
4. What fraction has olives? $\frac{1}{10}$
5. What fraction has mushrooms? $\frac{2}{10}$

Page 15

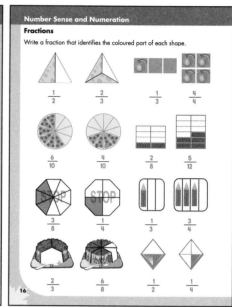

Number Sense and Numeration

Fractions

Write a fraction that identifies the coloured part of each shape.

$\frac{1}{2}$ $\frac{2}{3}$ $\frac{1}{3}$ $\frac{4}{4}$

$\frac{6}{10}$ $\frac{4}{10}$ $\frac{2}{8}$ $\frac{5}{12}$

$\frac{3}{8}$ $\frac{1}{4}$ $\frac{1}{3}$ $\frac{3}{4}$

$\frac{2}{3}$ $\frac{6}{8}$ $\frac{1}{2}$ $\frac{1}{4}$

Page 16

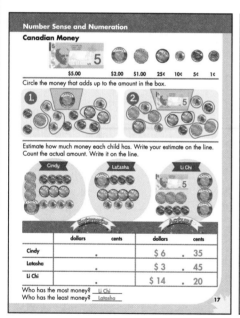

Number Sense and Numeration

Canadian Money

$5.00 $2.00 $1.00   25¢   10¢   5¢   1¢

Circle the money that adds up to the amount in the box.

1.   2.

Estimate how much money each child has. Write your estimate on the line. Count the actual amount. Write it on the line.

Cindy   Latasha   Li Chi

	dollars	cents	dollars	cents
Cindy		.	$ 6	. 35
Latasha		.	$ 3	. 45
Li Chi		.	$ 14	. 20

Who has the most money? __Li Chi__
Who has the least money? __Latasha__

Page 17

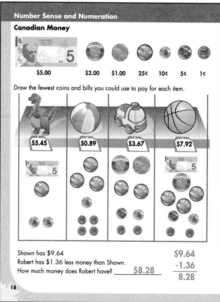

Number Sense and Numeration

Canadian Money

$5.00 $2.00 $1.00   25¢   10¢   5¢   1¢

Draw the fewest coins and bills you could use to pay for each item.

$5.45 $0.89 $3.67 $7.92

Shawn has $9.64
Robert has $1.36 less money than Shawn.
How much money does Robert have? __$8.28__

$9.64
-1.36
8.28

Page 18

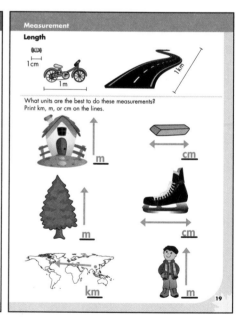

Measurement

Length

1cm   1m   1km

What units are the best to do these measurements?
Print km, m, or cm on the lines.

m   cm

m   cm

km   m

Page 19

58

Solutions

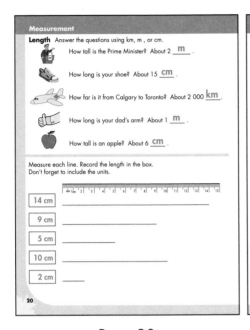

Measurement

Length Answer the questions using km , m , or cm.

How tall is the Prime Minister? About 2 __m__ .

How long is your shoe? About 15 __cm__ .

How far is it from Calgary to Toronto? About 2 000 __km__ .

How long is your dad's arm? About 1 __m__ .

How tall is an apple? About 6 __cm__ .

Measure each line. Record the length in the box.
Don't forget to include the units.

| 14 cm |
| 9 cm |
| 5 cm |
| 10 cm |
| 2 cm |

20

Page 20

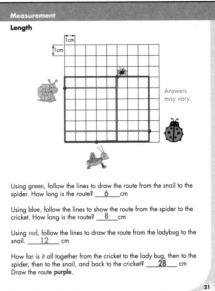

Measurement

Length

Answers may vary.

Using green, follow the lines to draw the route from the snail to the spider. How long is the route? __6__ cm

Using blue, follow the lines to show the route from the spider to the cricket. How long is the route? __8__ cm

Using red, follow the lines to draw the route from the ladybug to the snail. __12__ cm

How far is it all together from the cricket to the lady bug, then to the spider, then to the snail, and back to the cricket? __28__ cm
Draw the route purple.

21

Page 21

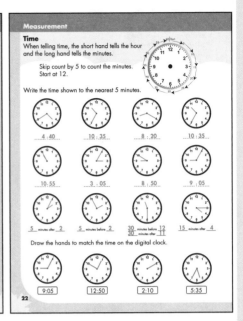

Measurement

Time
When telling time, the short hand tells the hour and the long hand tells the minutes.

Skip count by 5 to count the minutes. Start at 12.

Write the time shown to the nearest 5 minutes.

4 : 40   10 : 35   8 : 20   10 : 35

10 : 55   3 : 05   8 : 50   9 : 05

5 minutes after 2   5 minutes before 2   30 minutes before 12 / 30 minutes after 11   15 minutes after 4

Draw the hands to match the time on the digital clock.

9:05   12:50   2:10   5:35

22

Page 22

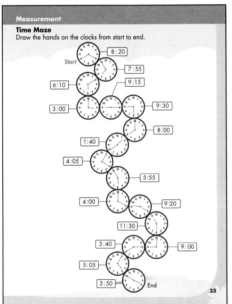

Measurement

Time Maze
Draw the hands on the clocks from start to end.

Start

8 : 20
7 : 55
6 : 10   9 : 15
3 : 00   9 : 30
8 : 00
1 : 40
4 : 05
5 : 55
4 : 00   9 : 20
11 : 30
3 : 40   9 : 00
5 : 05
3 : 50   End

23

Page 23

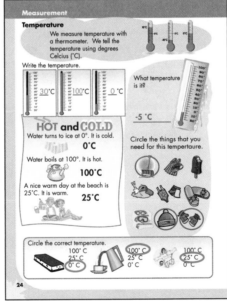

Measurement

Temperature
We measure temperature with a thermometer. We tell the temperature using degrees Celcius (°C).

Write the temperature.

30°C   100°C   0 °C

What temperature is it?

-5 °C

HOT and COLD
Water turns to ice at 0°. It is cold.   **0°C**

Water boils at 100°. It is hot.   **100°C**

A nice warm day at the beach is 25°C. It is warm.   **25°C**

Circle the things that you need for this tempertaure.

Circle the correct temperature.
100° C
25° C
0° C

100° C
25° C
0° C

100° C
25° C
0° C

24

Page 24

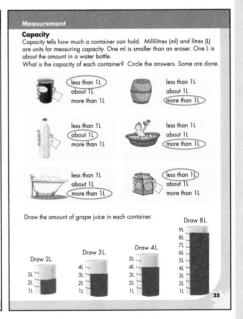

Measurement

Capacity
Capacity tells how much a container can hold. Millilitres (ml) and litres (L) are units for measuring capacity. One ml is smaller than an eraser. One L is about the amount in a water bottle.
What is the capacity of each container? Circle the answers. Some are done.

less than 1L / about 1L / more than 1L

less than 1L / about 1L / more than 1L

less than 1L / about 1L / more than 1L

less than 1L / about 1L / more than 1L

less than 1L / about 1L / more than 1L

less than 1L / about 1L / more than 1L

Draw the amount of grape juice in each container.

Draw 2L.   Draw 3L.   Draw 4L.   Draw 8L.

25

Page 25

Solutions

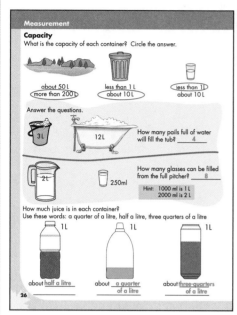

Measurement

Capacity
What is the capacity of each container? Circle the answer.

- about 50 L / (more than 200) / less than 1 L
- less than 1 L / (about 10 L)
- (less than 1 L) / about 10 L

Answer the questions.

3 L | 12 L — How many pails full of water will fill the tub? **4**

2 L | 250ml — How many glasses can be filled from the full pitcher? **8**

Hint: 1000 ml is 1 L
2000 ml is 2 L

How much juice is in each container?
Use these words: a quarter of a litre, half a litre, three quarters of a litre

- 1 L — about **half a litre**
- 1 L — about **a quarter of a litre**
- 1 L — about **three-quarters of a litre**

26

Page 26

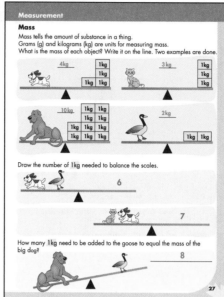

Measurement

Mass
Mass tells the amount of substance in a thing.
Grams (g) and kilograms (kg) are units for measuring mass.
What is the mass of each object? Write it on the line. Two examples are done.

- **4kg** — 1kg 1kg 1kg
- **3 kg** — 1kg 1kg 1kg
- **10 kg** — 1kg 1kg 1kg 1kg 1kg 1kg
- **2kg** — 1kg 1kg

Draw the number of 1kg needed to balance the scales.

- **6**
- **7**

How many 1kg need to be added to the goose to equal the mass of the big dog?
8

27

Page 27

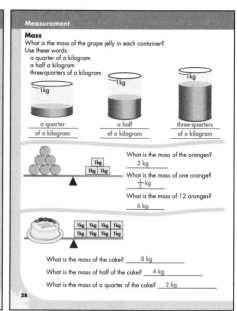

Measurement

Mass
What is the mass of the grape jelly in each container?
Use these words:
a quarter of a kilogram
a half a kilogram
three-quarters of a kilogram

- 1kg — **a quarter** of a kilogram
- 1kg — **a half** of a kilogram
- 1kg — **three-quarters** of a kilogram

1kg 1kg 1kg — What is the mass of the oranges? **3 kg**
What is the mass of one orange? **$\frac{1}{2}$ kg**
What is the mass of 12 oranges? **6 kg**

1kg 1kg 1kg 1kg / 1kg 1kg 1kg 1kg

What is the mass of the cake? **8 kg**
What is the mass of half of the cake? **4 kg**
What is the mass of a quarter of the cake? **2 kg**

28

Page 28

Geometry and Spatial Sense

3-D Shapes

cube | sphere | cylinder | cone | rectangular prism

Colour the sphere shapes red.
Colour the cube shapes blue.
Colour the cylinder shapes green.
Colour the cone shapes orange.
Colour the rectangular prism shapes purple.

29

Page 29

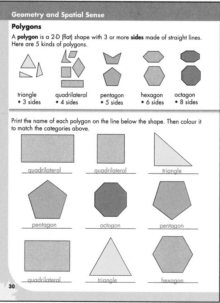

Geometry and Spatial Sense

Polygons
A **polygon** is a 2-D (flat) shape with 3 or more **sides** made of straight lines.
Here are 5 kinds of polygons.

triangle • 3 sides | quadrilateral • 4 sides | pentagon • 5 sides | hexagon • 6 sides | octagon • 8 sides

Print the name of each polygon on the line below the shape. Then colour it to match the categories above.

- **quadrilateral**
- **quadrilateral**
- **triangle**
- **pentagon**
- **octagon**
- **pentagon**
- **quadrilateral**
- **triangle**
- **hexagon**

30

Page 30

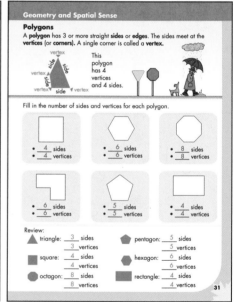

Geometry and Spatial Sense

Polygons
A **polygon** has 3 or more straight **sides** or **edges**. The sides meet at the **vertices (or corners)**. A single corner is called a **vertex**.

This polygon has 4 vertices and 4 sides.

Fill in the number of sides and vertices for each polygon.

- **4** sides / **4** vertices
- **6** sides / **6** vertices
- **8** sides / **8** vertices
- **6** sides / **6** vertices
- **5** sides / **5** vertices
- **4** sides / **4** vertices

Review:
- triangle: **3** sides / **3** vertices
- pentagon: **5** sides / **5** vertices
- square: **4** sides / **4** vertices
- hexagon: **6** sides / **6** vertices
- octagon: **8** sides / **8** vertices
- rectangle: **4** sides / **4** vertices

31

Page 31

Solutions

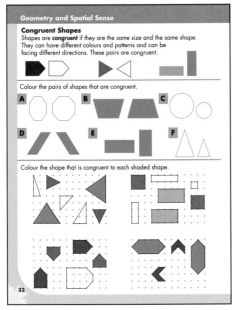

Page 32

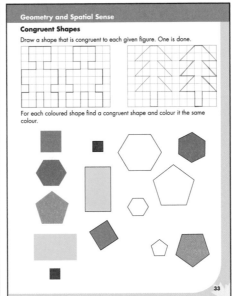

Page 33

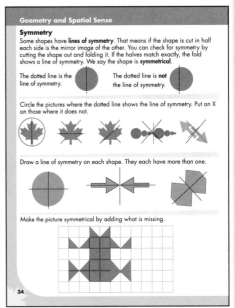

Page 34

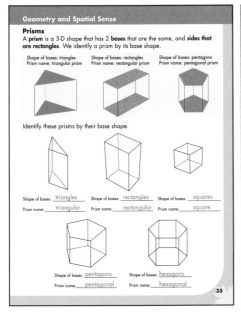

Page 35

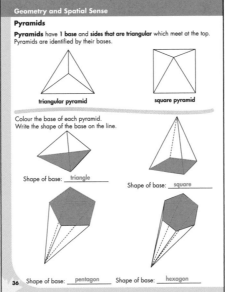

Page 36

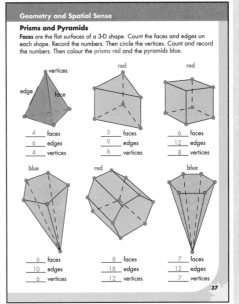

Page 37

Solutions

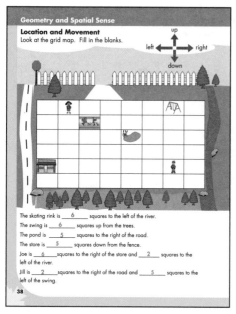

Page 38

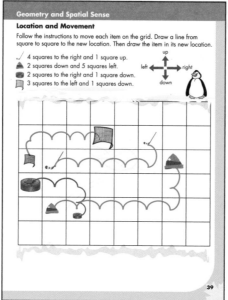

Page 39

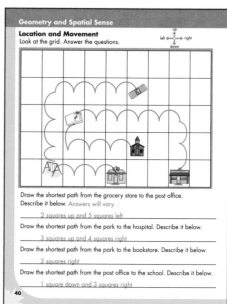

Page 40

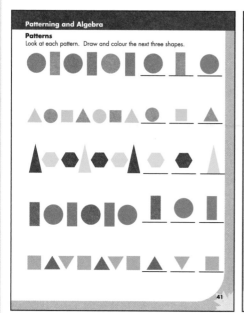

Page 41

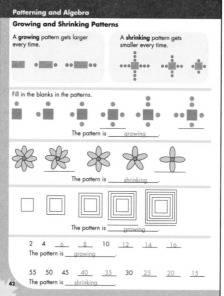

Page 42

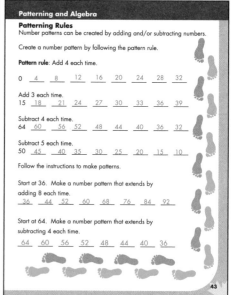

Page 43

Solutions

Page 44

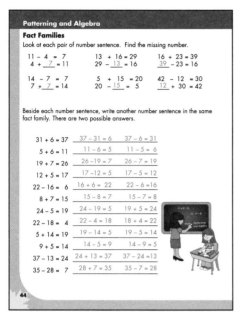

Patterning and Algebra

Fact Families

Look at each pair of number sentence. Find the missing number.

$11 - 4 = 7$ $13 + 16 = 29$ $16 + 23 = 39$
$4 + 7 = 11$ $29 - 13 = 16$ $39 - 23 = 16$

$14 - 7 = 7$ $5 + 15 = 20$ $42 - 12 = 30$
$7 + 7 = 14$ $20 - 15 = 5$ $12 + 30 = 42$

Beside each number sentence, write another number sentence in the same fact family. There are two possible answers.

$31 + 6 = 37$ $37 - 31 = 6$ $37 - 6 = 31$
$5 + 6 = 11$ $11 - 6 = 5$ $11 - 5 = 6$
$19 + 7 = 26$ $26 - 19 = 7$ $26 - 7 = 19$
$12 + 5 = 17$ $17 - 12 = 5$ $17 - 5 = 12$
$22 - 16 = 6$ $16 + 6 = 22$ $22 - 6 = 16$
$8 + 7 = 15$ $15 - 8 = 7$ $15 - 7 = 8$
$24 - 5 = 19$ $24 - 19 = 5$ $19 + 5 = 24$
$22 - 18 = 4$ $22 - 4 = 18$ $18 + 4 = 22$
$5 + 14 = 19$ $19 - 14 = 5$ $19 - 5 = 14$
$9 + 5 = 14$ $14 - 5 = 9$ $14 - 9 = 5$
$37 - 13 = 24$ $24 + 13 = 37$ $37 - 24 = 13$
$35 - 28 = 7$ $28 + 7 = 35$ $35 - 7 = 28$

44

Page 45

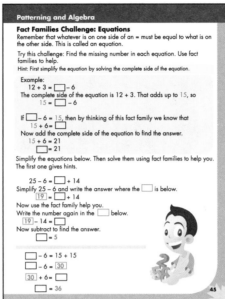

Patterning and Algebra

Fact Families Challenge: Equations

Remember that whatever is on one side of an = must be equal to what is on the other side. This is called an equation.

Try this challenge: Find the missing number in each equation. Use fact families to help.

Hint: First simplify the equation by solving the complete side of the equation.

Example:
$12 + 3 = \square - 6$
The complete side of the equation is $12 + 3$. That adds up to 15, so
$15 = \square - 6$

If $\square - 6 = 15$, then by thinking of this fact family we know that
$15 + 6 = \square$
Now add the complete side of the equation to find the answer.
$15 + 6 = 21$
$\square = 21$

Simplify the equations below. Then solve them using fact families to help you. The first one gives hints.

$25 - 6 = \square + 14$
Simplify $25 - 6$ and write the answer where the $\square$ is below.
$\boxed{19} = \square + 14$
Now use the fact family help you.
Write the number again in the $\square$ below.
$\boxed{19} - 14 = \square$
Now subtract to find the answer.
$\square = 5$

$\square - 6 = 15 + 15$
$\square - 6 = \boxed{30}$
$\boxed{30} + 6 = \square$
$\square = 36$

45

Page 46

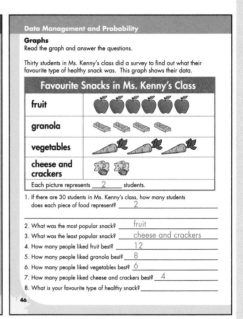

Data Management and Probability

Graphs

Read the graph and answer the questions.

Thirty students in Ms. Kenny's class did a survey to find out what their favourite type of healthy snack was. This graph shows their data.

Favourite Snacks in Ms. Kenny's Class

fruit	🍎🍎🍎🍎🍎🍎
granola	
vegetables	
cheese and crackers	

Each picture represents __2__ students.

1. If there are 30 students in Ms. Kenny's class, how many students does each piece of food represent? __2__
2. What was the most popular snack? __fruit__
3. What was the least popular snack? __cheese and crackers__
4. How many people liked fruit best? __12__
5. How many people liked granola best? __8__
6. How many people liked vegetables best? __6__
7. How many people liked cheese and crackers best? __4__
8. What is your favourite type of healthy snack? _____

46

Page 47

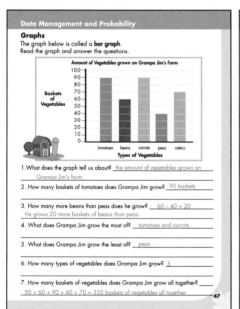

Data Management and Probability

Graphs

The graph below is called a **bar graph**.
Read the graph and answer the questions.

Amount of Vegetables grown on Grampa Jim's Farm

(Baskets of Vegetables: tomatoes, beans, carrots, peas, celery — Types of Vegetables)

1. What does the graph tell us about? __the amount of vegetables grown on Grampa Jim's farm.__
2. How many baskets of tomatoes does Grampa Jim grow? __90 baskets__
3. How many more beans than peas does he grow? __$60 - 40 = 20$__
   He grows 20 more baskets of beans than peas.
4. What does Grampa Jim grow the most of? __tomatoes and carrots__
5. What does Grampa Jim grow the least of? __peas__
6. How many types of vegetables does Grampa Jim grow? __5__
7. How many baskets of vegetables does Grampa Jim grow all together? ____
   $90 + 60 + 90 + 40 + 70 = 350$ baskets of vegetables all together

47

Page 48

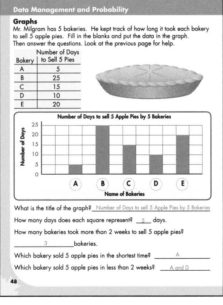

Data Management and Probability

Graphs

Mr. Milgram has 5 bakeries. He kept track of how long it took each bakery to sell 5 apple pies. Fill in the blanks and put the data in the graph. Then answer the questions. Look at the previous page for help.

Bakery	Number of Days to Sell 5 Pies
A	5
B	25
C	15
D	10
E	20

Number of Days to sell 5 Apple Pies by 5 Bakeries

(Number of Days — Name of Bakeries: A, B, C, D, E)

What is the title of the graph? __Number of Days to sell 5 Apple Pies by 5 Bakeries__

How many days does each square represent? __5__ days.

How many bakeries took more than 2 weeks to sell 5 apple pies? __3__ bakeries.

Which bakery sold 5 apple pies in the shortest time? __A__

Which bakery sold 5 apple pies in less than 2 weeks? __A and D__

48

Page 49

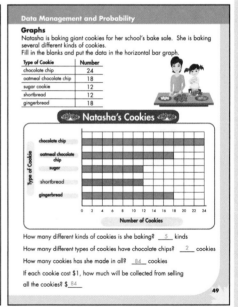

Data Management and Probability

Graphs

Natasha is baking giant cookies for her school's bake sale. She is baking several different kinds of cookies.
Fill in the blanks and put the data in the horizontal bar graph.

Type of Cookie	Number
chocolate chip	24
oatmeal chocolate chip	18
sugar cookie	12
shortbread	12
gingerbread	18

Natasha's Cookies

(Type of Cookie: chocolate chip, oatmeal chocolate chip, sugar, shortbread, gingerbread — Number of Cookies)

How many different kinds of cookies is she baking? __5__ kinds

How many different types of cookies have chocolate chips? __2__ cookies

How many cookies has she made in all? __84__ cookies

If each cookie cost $1, how much will be collected from selling all the cookies? $__84__

49

Solutions

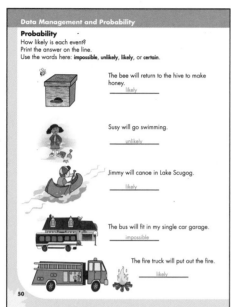

Page 50

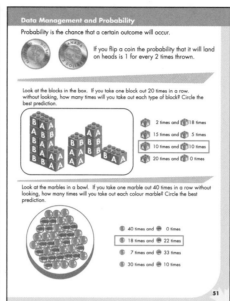

Page 51

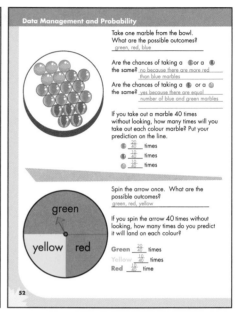

Page 52

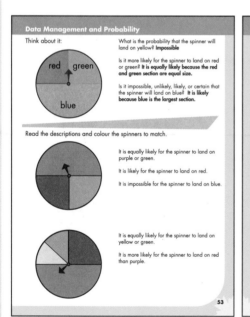

Page 53

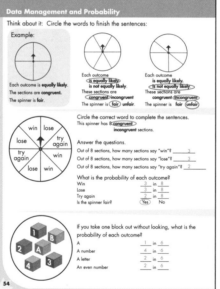

Page 54

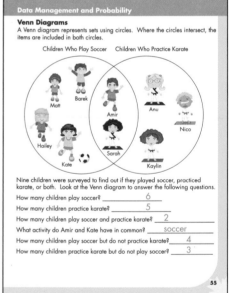

Page 55